nail
art

nail
art

create
over
50
nail
designs

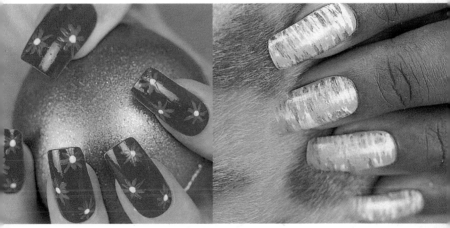

Pansy Alexander

CARLTON

THIS IS A CARLTON BOOK

Text, design and photographs copyright
© 1999 Carlton Books Limited

This edition published by Carlton Books Limited 1999
20 St Anne's Court
Wardour Street
London W1V 3AW

A CIP catalogue for this book is available from the
British Library.

ISBN 1 85868 691 1

Senior Executive Editor: Venetia Penfold
Art Director: Penny Stock
Editor: Zia Mattocks
Designer: Barbara Zuñiga
Photographer: Janine Hosegood
Production: Alexia Turner

Printed in Italy.

Contents

Introduction to Nail Art

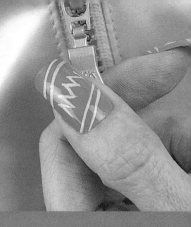

Nail art is a fabulous way to create funky new looks for your fingertips, and lets you have fun experimenting with patterns and colours, treating your nails as a blank canvas. The following collection of cool nail designs is based on current fashion trends and illustrates all the basic techniques you need to master to create amazing talons. Each design idea is accompanied by a list of the materials you'll need – the different coloured nail polishes and paints and advice on the types of brushes you should use, together with any transfers, striping tape, stick-on designs or rhinestones – and clear step-by-step instructions on how to achieve the look.

Your basic nail-art kit should include a good range of nail polishes and water-based paints in various colours, a selection of brushes and a

special-effects tool, together with striping tape, transfers, stencils, polish secures and nail-art sealer to protect your finished designs. For filling in large areas of colour use nail polish and for adding more intricate details use water-based paints applied with a very fine paint brush; if you want to paint perfect straight lines, use a striping brush.

plastic nail tips

Plastic nail tips are ideal if your own nails aren't long enough to paint on. The tips cover the natural nail and are tapered to fit under the cuticle. They are either flat or curved, with square, round or oval tips. The advantage is that you can paint the design before applying them to your nails – you can also use them to practise your nail art.

❤ Select the correct size, making sure they fit over the entire nail.

❤ Place a drop of glue on the underside of the tip, press it firmly onto the nail and hold it for 30 seconds. If the glue comes in contact with the skin, use an acetone-based polish remover to melt it away.

❤ Never pull the tips off; always use an acetone-based polish remover.

caring for your hands

Keeping your hands and cuticles moisturized and nourished is the key to having soft hands and healthy, strong nails, and there are a few simple procedures you can follow to keep them in peak condition.

❤ Always dry your hands thoroughly when you wash them.

❤ Regularly use a moisturizing hand lotion and massage it well into the skin, especially around the cuticles.

❤ Wear protective gloves when using cleaning products.

❤ Use a non-acetone nail-polish remover, but don't use it more than once a week as it strips and weakens the nails.

❤ Remember not to file your nails more than is necessary, and always work in one direction only to avoid weakening the nails.

conditioning
manicure

You don't have to visit a salon to have gorgeous, pampered nails. It takes just a few minutes to perform a basic mini-manicure at home to keep your nails in top condition. Try to do this once a month.

❤ Massage the skin around the nail using a good cuticle cream, then soak the fingers in warm water with a soap-free cleanser for 1–2 minutes.

❤ Wrap the end of an orange-wood stick with cotton wool. Dip it in the warm water and gently rub the edges of the nail plate to remove any dead cuticle.

❤ Dry the hands thoroughly and apply some nourishing hand cream, massaging it in well.

❤ Working in one direction, shape your nails into rounded, square or 'squoval' tips, using a soft to normal emery board – if the emery board is too hard it will cause flaking and chipping at the edge of the nail. Never use an emery board across the surface of the nail plate.

❤ To prevent coloured polish from staining your nails, and to help strengthen them and smooth ridges, always apply two coats of an all-in-one conditioning base coat, strengthener and top coat.

❤ Paint your nails with two coats of polish, allowing each to dry naturally before applying the next.

❤ Apply a top coat of clear varnish to seal the colour and help prevent chipping. 'Lift' the nails every other day with a further coat of top glaze.

nail
polishes

Nail polish comes in a vast array of fabulous colours from classic flat colours to up-to-the-minute metallic, pearlized and iridescent shades, including two-tone polishes and glitter varnishes, which are great for parties. You will need a good range of your favourite nail polishes to act as base colours for your designs. In addition to the prerequisite reds and pinks, you should have nail polishes in black, white, green, blue and yellow. For special effects, you should have

gold and silver metallic polishes and a couple of glitter polishes.

Always buy small bottles of nail polish, since larger bottles become sticky and unusable after they've been around for a while. You should also always make sure you clean the rims of the bottles after using them to make sure you don't transfer dried flakes of polish onto the nails when you paint them.

First, shake the bottle or roll it between your palms to mix the polish. Taking care not to overload the brush, apply the first coat by making one stroke down the centre of the nail, then one on each side. Avoid touching the cuticle area with polish – leave a thin line around the edge of the nail. Let it dry completely and naturally, then apply a second coat to achieve smooth coverage without streaking.

nail
paints

These acrylic, water-based, non-toxic, quick-drying paints can be used to add pattern and detail to a base of nail polish. There are a huge range of colours, including fluorescents and opalescents, which are pearl-white but when used sparingly on a dark nail polish become a vibrant colour. You should have at least black, white, red, blue, green and yellow paints as a starting point, since these can be mixed to create other colours and shades. Place a small drop of paint on a palette and close the jar to keep it fresh (keep the lid and rim clean); always apply paint sparingly using a fine brush.

nail-art
brushes

Brushes should be used to apply nail paints, and you should have at least three different ones in your nail-art kit.

❤ Standard brush for creating the main features of your design.

❤ Fine-detail brush with short bristles tapering into a very fine tip for carrying out intricate work.

❤ Striping brush with long, even bristles for creating straight, well-defined lines or stripes.

❤ Fan brush with flat, fan-shaped bristles for carrying out feathering and other special effects.

❤ Special-effects tool – with a small, rounded metal tip for dotting, marbling and other special effects.

using stencils

Reusable stencils are a simple way of creating clean patterns. They are available in a range of designs and you can create your own by cutting tiny shapes out of a sheet of flexible card using a craft knife.

❤ Apply two coats of your chosen base polish and allow your nails to dry completely.

❤ Position the stencil and make sure it sits flat across the nail to keep the edges of the design clean.

❤ Hold it still and apply a small amount of paint with a make-up sponge; allow the paint to dry before you remove the stencil.

striping tape

Self-adhesive striping tape can be used to enhance designs or as a guide for painting straight lines. It comes in various colours and widths, from less than 1 mm wide to a wider tape that incorporates patterns, such as squares, hearts or diamonds.

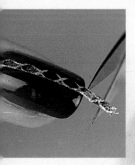

❤ Apply two coats of your chosen base polish and allow your nails to dry completely.

❤ Lay the tape across the nail, allowing a small amount to overhang the edge.

❤ Press the tape down and trim off the end.

❤ Cover the entire nail area with a top coat of nail-art sealer to protect the design.

nail
transfers

Transfers are either individual images or a series of elements that can be combined to create a larger design that runs across all the nails on one hand.

❤ Apply two coats of base polish and allow your nails to dry completely.

❤ Cut out the image, leaving just enough room around the edge of the transfer to hold it by.

❤ Apply a little water to the back of the transfer and wait for 30 seconds before sliding the design off the backing and into place on the nail. Press it gently to make sure it is dry and lying flat.

❤ Add a top coat of protective nail-art sealer.

stick-on
patterns

Stick-on patterns come in the form of self-adhesive sheets, which can be cut to size and simply stuck on the nail.

❤ Lay the self-adhesive sheet in position over the nail and, using an orange-wood stick, mark the outline of the nail, following the curve of the cuticle.

❤ Neatly cut out the shape, remove the backing and stick it on the nail, making sure it lies flat with no air bubbles.

❤ Add a top coat of protective nail-art sealer.

rhinestones
& polish secures

For a touch of glamour and sparkle,
incorporate rhinestones or polish
secures – tiny stones, gems, studs
and jewels – into your nail
designs. These are available
in a wide range of shapes, styles and colours,
including foil shapes such as stars, hearts and circles.

❤ Apply two coats of your chosen polish and, when it is dry, apply
a coat of clear varnish where you want to place the polish secures.

❤ Position the secures on the wet polish; as the polish dries, they
will set in place. To position stones in a straight line, first lay a piece
of damp cotton across the wet polish to create a guideline, remove
the cotton and place the stones on the wet polish, following the line.

❤ Cover the nail with a top coat of protective nail-art sealer.

nail-art
sealer

Water-based nail paints, striping tape, stick-on designs and transfers
will readily come off when you wash unless they are protected by a
top coat. Any nail-polish protector or top-coat glaze will work to
seal these elements. However, specialized nail-art sealer is heavier
than standard top coat, and this should always be used when
polish secures are incorporated into a design to help prevent
them from coming loose from the nail.

french
manicure

FLESH-PINK AND WHITE POLISHES

❤ Over a base coat, apply two coats of natural-looking flesh-pink polish and, while it is tacky, lay a length of damp cotton on the tips of the nails to mark a guideline for the edge of the white area; remove the cotton and let the polish dry.

❤ Define the tips with two coats of white polish and let it dry.

❤ Finish by applying a top coat of nail-art sealer.

glitter
glamour

ONE-COAT GLITTER POLISHES IN PURPLE, GOLD, BLUE, RED AND GREEN

- ♥ Over a base coat, apply one coat of glitter polish, using a different colour for each nail, and allow it to dry.

- ♥ Finish by applying a top coat of nail-art sealer to help preserve the polish and prevent it from chipping.

chinoiserie
chic

GOLD/RED POLISH • BLACK PAINT OR CHINESE CHARACTER TRANSFERS

❤ Over a base coat, apply two coats of gold or red polish; let it dry.

❤ Using a fine-detail brush, paint the character of your choice
   in black paint (practise it on paper first). Alternatively, use
   Chinese character transfers. Do this on every finger or just
   the thumb and the second and fourth fingers.

❤ When the nails are dry, apply a top coat of nail-art sealer.

Japanese
daisies

DARK PURPLE POLISH • LILAC, BRIGHT PINK AND GREEN PAINTS

❤ Over a base coat, apply two coats of purple polish; let it dry.

❤ Using a fine-detail brush, paint the pink and lilac flowers. Paint the centre of each flower first, then add the petals, giving the pink flowers lilac centres and the lilac flowers pink centres.

❤ Finish off the design by adding the green leaves.

❤ When the nails are dry, apply a top coat of nail-art sealer.

fabulous
flowers

MID-PURPLE POLISH • SILVER METAL OVALS • CLEAR RHINESTONES

- ❤ Over a base coat, apply two coats of purple polish; let it dry.

- ❤ Apply a top coat of clear varnish to the centre of the nail.

- ❤ Place the rhinestone in the wet polish in the centre of the nail and arrange the metal ovals around it, so they radiate from it.

- ❤ When the nails are dry and the polish secures are set in place, apply a protective top coat of nail-art sealer.

animal
kingdom

MID-BLUE/SILVER POLISH • DARK BLUE/BLACK PAINT

- ❤ Over a base coat, apply two coats of blue or silver polish; let it dry.
- ❤ Use a striping brush to paint the zebra stripes; work across the nail from one side to the other and make some stripes thicker than others. Paint dark blue stripes on the mid-blue polish and black stripes on the silver polish.
- ❤ When the nails are dry, apply a top coat of nail-art sealer.

love
hearts

RED POLISH • STICK-ON GOLD AND SILVER FOIL HEARTS

❤ Over a base coat, apply two coats of red polish and let it dry.

❤ Position three stick-on foil hearts diagonally down the centre
of the nail on the thumb and the second and fourth fingers.

❤ Apply a top coat of nail-art sealer to protect the hearts.

sea
spray

LIGHT BLUE POLISH • 'WAVES' TRANSFERS

- ❤ Over a base coat, apply two coats of blue polish and let it dry.
- ❤ Cut out the transfer, apply a drop of water to the back and wait for 30 seconds before sliding the transfer off its backing and into position on the tip of the nail.
- ❤ When the transfers are dry and have set in place, apply a protective top coat of nail-art sealer.

starry
nights

BLACK/SILVER POLISH • SILVER/DARK PURPLE PAINT

- ❤ Over a base coat, apply two coats of black or silver polish and allow it to dry.
- ❤ Use a fine-detail brush to paint the stars; paint silver stars on the black polish and dark purple stars on the silver polish.
- ❤ When the nails are completely dry, apply a top coat of nail-art sealer.

eastern
promise

ORANGE POLISH • SELF-ADHESIVE NAIL BINDIS

- ❤ Over a base coat, apply two coats of orange polish and allow it to dry.
- ❤ Position the self-adhesive bindis on the tip of the nail, placing them on the thumb and the second and fourth fingers.
- ❤ Apply a top coat of nail-art sealer to protect the bindis.

oriental
fronds

BLACK POLISH · RED PAINT

- ❤ Over a base coat, apply two coats of black polish and allow it to dry.
- ❤ Use a striping brush to paint the red fronds on the thumb and the second and fourth fingers.
- ❤ When the nails are completely dry, apply a top coat of nail-art sealer.

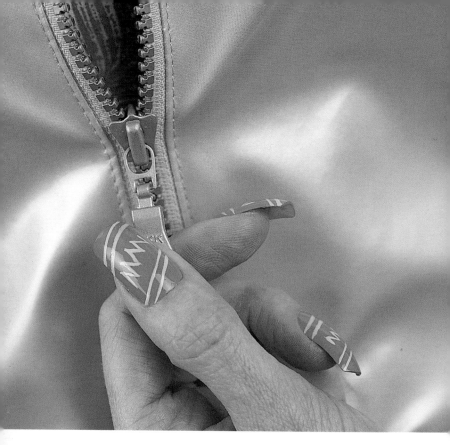

tribal
chic

BRIGHT BLUE/MOSS-GREEN POLISH • PALE PINK/BLACK AND GREEN PAINTS

- ❤ Over a base coat, apply two coats of blue or green polish; let it dry.
- ❤ For the blue design, use a striping brush to paint four parallel pink diagonals, then the central zigzag. For the green design, use a striping brush to paint the two straight lines, and a fine-detail brush for the triangular shapes and to fill in the pattern.
- ❤ When the nails are dry, add a top coat of nail-art sealer.

checkmate
queen

RED AND BLACK POLISHES • BLACK-AND-GOLD CHECK TRANSFER

- ❤ Over a base coat, apply two coats of red polish to ¾ of the nail and, when dry, paint the tips black; allow the nails to dry.
- ❤ Add a drop of water to the back of the transfer, wait for 30 seconds, then position the strip horizontally over the join.
- ❤ When the transfer is dry and set in place, trim the ends flush with the nail and apply a top coat of nail-art sealer.

american
dream

WHITE POLISH • RED, WHITE AND BLUE PAINTS

❤ Over a base coat, apply two coats of white polish and let it dry.

❤ Use a striping brush to paint horizontal red stripes across the central part of the nail and allow it to dry.

❤ Use a standard brush to paint the blue square and let it dry.

❤ Paint the white stars on the blue square with a fine-detail brush.

❤ When the nails are dry, apply a top coat of nail-art sealer.

razzle
dazzle

BLUE POLISH · CLEAR RHINESTONES

- ❤ Over a base coat, apply two coats of blue polish and let it dry.

- ❤ Paint on a top coat of clear varnish and, while it is still wet, use a special-effects tool to position the rhinestones in your chosen configuration on the nails.

- ❤ When the nails are completely dry and the rhinestones are set in place, apply a protective top coat of nail-art sealer.

declaration
of love

WHITE POLISH • 'I LOVE YOU' TRANSFERS

❤ Over a base coat, apply two coats of white polish; let it dry.

❤ Cut out the transfers, apply a drop of water to the backing and wait for 30 seconds before sliding the transfer into position on the nail.

❤ When the transfers are dry and have set in place, apply a protective top coat of nail-art sealer.

disco
diva

BRIGHT BLUE AND RAINBOW DROPS (TRANSLUCENT GLITTER) POLISHES

- ♥ Over a base coat, apply two coats of bright blue polish and allow it to dry.
- ♥ Paint one coat of translucent glitter polish over the top and leave it to dry.
- ♥ To finish, apply a top coat of nail-art sealer to protect the polish and help prevent it from chipping.

35

camouflage
mania

GOLD/BRIGHT BLUE POLISH • ORANGE, BLACK AND WHITE/WHITE,
DARK BLUE AND MID-BLUE PAINTS

❤ Over a base coat, apply two coats of gold or blue polish; let it dry.

❤ On the gold, use a standard brush for the orange shapes, then
add the black and white details with a fine brush. On the blue,
outline the shapes in white, then fill them in with the two blues.

❤ When the nails are dry, apply a top coat of nail-art sealer.

lost in
space

BLACK POLISH • SILVER STRIPING TAPE • CLEAR RHINESTONES

- ❤ Over a base coat, apply two coats of black polish and let it dry.
- ❤ Use striping tape to form two double crosses, one at the base of the nail and one at the tip, then trim off the ends of the tape.
- ❤ Apply a drop of clear varnish in the centre of the cross at the tip of the nail and position the rhinestone on the wet polish.
- ❤ When it has set, apply a protective top coat of nail-art sealer.

stained-glass
magic

ONE-COAT GLITTER POLISHES IN GOLD, SILVER, PURPLE, PINK, BLUE

AND GREEN • WHITE AND BLACK PAINTS

- ❤ After applying a base coat, use a standard brush to outline the
  shapes with diluted white paint on the thumb and two fingers.
- ❤ Avoiding the outlines, fill in the shapes with glitter polish and
  apply gold glitter polish to the first and third fingers; let it dry.
- ❤ Define the outlines in black paint, then coat with nail-art sealer.

sugar
candy

PALE GREEN/PALE YELLOW POLISH • WHITE, DARK GREEN, PALE YELLOW

AND ORANGE/PALE BLUE, PALE PINK, WHITE AND PALE YELLOW PAINTS

- ❤ Over a base coat, apply two coats of pale green or pale yellow polish and allow it to dry.
- ❤ Use a striping brush to paint narrow horizontal stripes across the nail, alternating the colours.
- ❤ When the nails are dry, apply a top coat of nail-art sealer.

41

serpent's
embrace

SNAKESKIN STICK-ON SHEETS

❤ After applying a base coat, position the snakeskin sheet over the nail and, using an orange-wood stick, mark the outline of the nail, following the curve of the cuticle.

❤ Neatly cut out the shape, remove the backing and position it on the nail, making sure it lies flat without any air bubbles.

❤ Apply a protective top coat of nail-art sealer.

jungle
fever

WHITE AND BLACK POLISHES • BLACK AND WHITE PAINTS

- ❤ Over a base coat, apply two coats of white polish to the thumb and the second and fourth fingers, then two coats of black polish to the first and third fingers; allow it to dry.

- ❤ Using a fine-detail brush, paint the tiger-print shapes on the nails in the contrasting colour; do the outlines first, then fill them in.

- ❤ When the nails are dry, apply a top coat of nail-art sealer.

flower
power

-BRIGHT YELLOW/BRIGHT BLUE POLISH • WHITE, DARK YELLOW AND
GREEN/WHITE, PALE BLUE AND DARK YELLOW PAINTS

- ❤ Over a base coat, apply two coats of yellow or blue polish; let it dry.
- ❤ Using a special-effects tool, for the yellow design, paint white petals, then yellow centres and, lastly, the leaves. For the blue design, paint white and blue petals, then the yellow centres.
- ❤ When the nails are dry, apply a top coat of nail-art sealer.

artist's
easel

PALE BLUE POLISH • WHITE, BRIGHT PINK AND OPALESCENT BLUE PAINTS

❤ Over a base coat, apply two coats of blue polish and let it dry.

❤ Apply the white paint first, using a fan brush to feather it across the nail from each side to the centre. Before it dries, apply the pink paint, fanning it across the nail in the same way; let it dry.

❤ Apply one coat of opalescent blue paint, and, when the nails are dry, finish with a top coat of nail-art sealer.

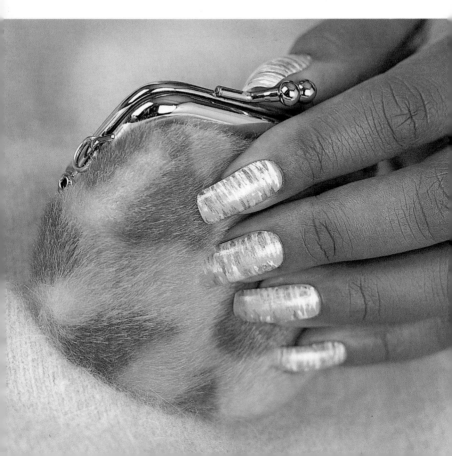

perfect
pastels

PASTEL BLUE, PINK, GREEN AND YELLOW POLISHES • WHITE PAINT

• BLUE, PINK, GREEN AND YELLOW RHINESTONES

❤ Over a base coat, paint each nail a different colour and let it dry.

❤ Using a standard brush, paint the white daisies and V-shaped tips.

❤ Apply a drop of top coat and use a special-effects tool to position matching rhinestones in the centre of the daisies.

❤ When the nails are dry, apply a top coat of nail-art sealer.

french
connection

MAGENTA GLITTER AND BRIGHT PINK/MINT-GREEN AND DARK GREEN

GLITTER POLISHES • SILVER STRIPING TAPE/MID-GREEN PAINT

❤ Over a base coat, apply two coats of magenta glitter to ¾ of the

   nail and paint the tips pink; when dry, lay striping tape over the join.

❤ Or, apply two coats of mint; when dry, create a 'V' on the tips

   in green glitter, then define the 'V' in green with a striping brush.

❤ When the nails are dry, apply a top coat of nail-art sealer.

dancing
dolphins

BRIGHT YELLOW POLISH • 'DOLPHINS' TRANSFERS

💙 Over a base coat, apply two coats of yellow polish; let it dry.

💙 Cut out the dolphin transfers, apply a drop of water to the backing and wait for 30 seconds before sliding the transfer into position on the thumb and the second and fourth fingers.

💙 When the transfers are dry and have set in place, apply a protective top coat of nail-art sealer.

tropicana
paradise

WHITE POLISH • 'PALM SPRINGS' TRANSFERS

- Over a base coat, apply two coats of white polish; let it dry.
- Cut out the palm transfers, apply a drop of water to the backing and wait for 30 seconds before sliding a transfer into position on each nail, with the base of the transfer close to the tip.
- When the transfers are dry and have set in place, apply a protective top coat of nail-art sealer.

cool
love

BRIGHT PINK/PURPLE POLISH • PALE BLUE/LILAC PAINT • LETTER STENCILS

- ❤ Over a base coat, apply two coats of pink or purple polish; let it dry.
- ❤ Position the stencils flat against the nails and apply a little paint at a time using a make-up sponge; paint pale blue letters on pink nails and pale lilac letters on purple nails.
- ❤ Wait until the paint is completely dry, then remove the stencils and apply a top coat of nail-art sealer.

shades
of grey

BLACK POLISH • WHITE PAINT

❤ This graduated stripe is achieved by airbrushing, which can only be done in a salon; to imitate the look, apply a base coat, then paint two coats of black nail polish and leave it to dry.

❤ Dilute some white paint and paint four diagonal stripes, each progressively lighter in colour, finishing with a white stripe.

❤ When the nails are dry, apply a top coat of nail-art sealer.

rose
garden

RED POLISH • 'TEARS OF ROSES' TRANSFERS

- ❤ Over a base coat, apply two coats of red polish and let it dry.
- ❤ Cut out the rose transfers, apply a drop of water to the backing and wait for 30 seconds before sliding the transfer into position on the tip of the nail.
- ❤ When the transfers are dry and have set in place, apply a protective top coat of nail-art sealer.

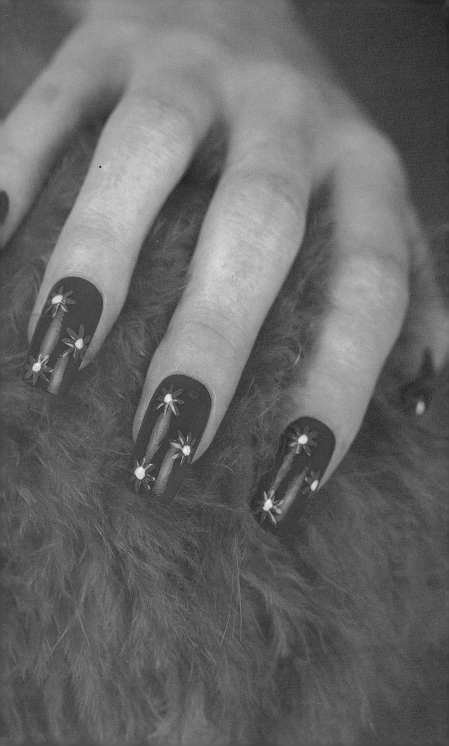

starflower **frenzy**

BLUE/BRIGHT PINK POLISH • BRIGHT PINK AND YELLOW/BLUE AND

YELLOW PAINTS

- ❤ Over a base coat, apply two coats of blue or pink polish; let it dry.
- ❤ Using a fine-detail brush, paint pink stars on the blue nails and blue stars on the pink nails, and allow the paint to dry.
- ❤ Using a special-effects tool, give the stars yellow centres.
- ❤ When the nails are dry, apply a top coat of nail-art sealer.

think
pink

BRIGHT PINK POLISH • WHITE PAINT

- ♥ Over a base coat, apply two coats of bright pink polish and allow it to dry.
- ♥ Use a striping brush to paint diagonal white stripes, working across the top of the nail and leaving the tip pink.
- ♥ When the nails are dry, apply a top coat of nail-art sealer.

retro
stars

WHITE POLISH • BLACK PAINT • STENCIL CIRCLE • WHITE STICK-ON STARS

- ❤ This is an airbrush design, which can only be done in a salon; to imitate it, apply a base coat, then two coats of white polish.

- ❤ When dry, position the stencil in the centre of the nail and fill in the circle with black paint; let it dry, then remove the stencil.

- ❤ Apply the self-adhesive star to the centre of the black circle.

- ❤ When the nails are dry, apply a top coat of nail-art sealer.

cool
britannia

LILAC/BLUE POLISH • PURPLE/RED AND WHITE PAINTS

- ❤ Over a base coat, apply two coats of lilac or blue polish; let it dry.

- ❤ On the blue, use a striping brush to paint thick vertical, horizontal and diagonal red lines, crossing in the centre of the nail. When dry, use a fine-detail brush to add a white outline. On the lilac, paint the outline shape in purple, starting with two vertical lines.

- ❤ When the nails are dry, apply a top coat of nail-art sealer.

ring the
changes

BLACK POLISH • WHITE PAINT • NAIL RING

- ❤ Over a base coat, apply two coats of black nail polish; let it dry.
- ❤ Pierce the nail with a nail drill or have it done in a salon (if your nail is not thick and strong, apply a plastic tip and pierce that).
- ❤ Use a striping brush to paint four white lines, feathering out from the edge of the hole over the tip of the nail.
- ❤ When dry, apply a top coat of nail-art sealer and insert the ring.

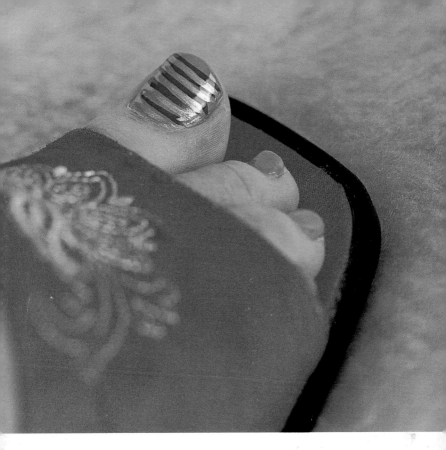

feet for
dancing

BRIGHT PINK POLISH • PURPLE AND GOLD PAINTS

- ♥ Over a base coat, apply two coats of bright pink polish and allow it to dry.
- ♥ On the big toe only, use a striping brush to paint horizontal, evenly spaced stripes, alternating between gold and purple.
- ♥ When the nails are dry, apply a top coat of nail-art sealer.

Resources

Pansy Alexander
Nails to Go
48–52 Kensington
    High Street
London W8 4PE
0171 795 6333
*Nail salon and supplier
of nail-art products
and accessories,
including all those
featured in this book.
Call for mail order.*

Boots Company PLC
(head office)
Nottingham
NG90 1BS
0115 9506111
*Stockists of a range of
nail-art products and
accessories. Call for
your nearest branch.*

Claire's Accessories
(head office)
2 Pennine Way
Saltley Business Park
Saltley
Birmingham B8 1JW
0121 682 8000
*Stockists of nail-art prod-
ucts and accessories. Call
for your nearest branch.*

Harrods
87–135 Brompton Rd
London SW1X 7XL
0171 730 1234
*Stockist of nail-art
products and accessories.*

Harvey Nichols
109–25 Knightsbridge
London SW1X 7RG
0171 235 5000
*Stockist of nail-art
products and accessories.*

House of Fraser
(head office)
1 Howick Place
London SW1P 1BH
0171 963 2000
*Stockists of nail-art prod-
ucts and accessories. Call
for your nearest store.*

Miss Selfridge
1 Garrick Road
London NW9 6AU
0181 910 1100
*Stockists of nail-art
products and accessories.
Call for your nearest
branch.*

New Look Ltd
(head office)
Mercery Road
Weymouth
Dorset DT3 5HJ
01305 761155
*Stockists of nail-art
products and accessories.
Call for your nearest
branch.*

Salon System
Ventura House
Bullsbrook Road
Hayes
Middlesex UB4 0UJ
0181 573 9907
Mail order 0800 146298
*Supplier of nail-art
products and accessories.
Call for your nearest
stockist.*

Screenface
48 Monmouth Street
London WC2 9ET
0171 836 3955
*Stockist of nail-art
products and accessories.*

Screenface
24 Powis Terrace
London W11 1JH
0171 221 8289
*Stockist of nail-art
products and accessories.*

Selfridges
Oxford Street
London W1A 1AB
0171 629 1234
*Stockist of nail-art
products and accessories.*

Superdrug Stores PLC
(head office)
118 Beddington Lane
Croydon
Surrey CR0 4TB
0181 684 7000
*Stockists of nail-art
products and accessories.
Call for your nearest
branch.*

Top Shop
(head office)
Colegrave House
70 Berners Street
London W1P 3AE
0171 636 8040
*Stockists of nail-art prod-
ucts and accessories. Call
for your nearest branch.*

Zest
18 Broadwick Street
London W1V 1FG
0171 437 3846
*Stockist of nail-art
products and accessories.*

Zest
38 Upper Street
London N1 0PN
0171 704 6680
*Stockist of nail-art
products and accessories.*